Welcome to Ponyville!

Phidal

DELIGHTFUL AND DELICIOUS

Pinkie Pie loves working at SugarCube Corner. Today she's teaching Apple Bloom how to bake a cake. Will you help them? Place your stickers in the right spots.

Cake Pan

Sugar

Measuring Cup

Bowl

Eggs

Flour

Cool Cutie Marks

Do you recognize these cutie marks? Each one is unique! Match your pony stickers to the correct cutie marks.

Around Town

There's so much to see and do in Ponyville. If you're lucky, you just may see your friends! Place your stickers below to decorate the scene.

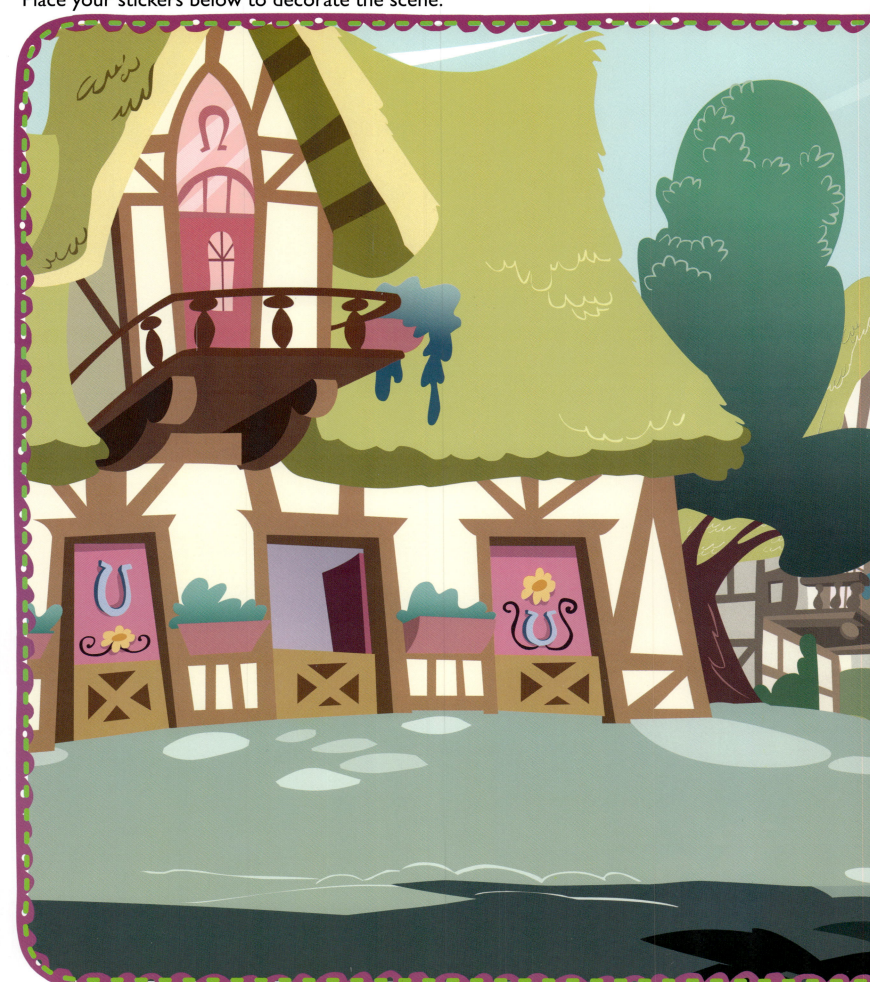

There's nowhere Twilight Sparkle would rather be than the Golden Oak Library! This smart pony loves learning new things. Use your stickers to decorate the library.

Fast Flier

Rainbow Dash sure loves to race! Find out who is cheering her on by placing your stickers below. On your marks, get set, go!

Counting on the Farm

There is so much to see and do at Sweet Apple Acres! What do you see? Count each item, and then place your number stickers in the right spots.

6

7

8

9

10

COLORFUL CREATURES

Gummy and the pony pals are so colorful! Using your stickers, place the friends with the matching colors, and then name each color.

Perfect Pets

Phidal

Pet Pair-Up

The ponies really love their pets! Do you know which pony goes with each pet? Pair up the pals by placing your stickers in the right spots.

Winona

Gummy

Tank

Angel

Owlowiscious

Opal

Pony Patterns

Take a look at each row of patterns below. Can you tell who's missing? Use your pony and pet stickers to complete the patterns.

Tic-Tac-Hooves

Twilight Sparkle and Applejack are playing a fun game of Tic-Tac-Hooves! Grab a friend and take turns playing with your stickers.

PONIES AND PETS

These pony pals and their pets have gathered in the park. They always have lots of fun together! Decorate the scene with your stickers.

Sizing Up

Ponies, dragons, and animals come in all sorts of shapes and sizes! Using your stickers, place the creatures from smallest to largest.

Magic Mix-Up

Twilight Sparkle is practicing magic and creating some silly creatures! Use your stickers to see which pets were combined in each spell.

Pretty Pony

Fluttershy, Opal, and Angel think that Twilight looks lovely as she models Rarity's latest design. Use your stickers to recreate the scene in the space below.

Color Combos

How well do you know the pets of Ponyville? Take a look at the color combos below, and place your pet stickers in the right spots.

WHO DO YOU SEE?

The ponies are playing hide-and-seek with their pets. Can you spot anyone? Help Winona find her friends by placing your stickers below.

Fashion Time

Phidal

Dazzling Dresses

Rarity is hard at work making dresses at the Carousel Boutique. Aren't they all amazing? Everypony is sure to look great! Place your stickers below.

FASHION ADDITION

It's time for Rarity to count all of the sewing supplies in her store. Using your stickers, help her complete the equations below.

$1 + 1 = 2$

$3 + 2 = 5$

$1 + 2 = 3$

4 + 2 = 6

3 + 4 = 7

2 + 2 = 4

DELIGHTFUL DESIGNS

Hoity Toity has come to the Carousel Boutique to check out Rarity's latest designs. This fashionable pony is impressed! Decorate the scene with your stickers.

674

4 5

12

13

16

3

6 11

14 15

CUSTOM CLOTHES

Rarity is decorating these outfits to reflect the unique personalities of the ponies that will wear them. Place your stickers on the matching shadows.

I have a sweet tooth.

I love everything about spring.

I harvest apples at the farm.

I love to study magic.

I clear the clouds over Ponyville.

I am a creative pony.

A Smoky Day

There's a cloud of smoke covering Ponyville! Help Twilight Sparkle discover what's causing the smoke by reading the clues and placing your stickers below.

It has sharp claws…

It sleeps in a cave and snores…

It hoards treasure…

It has long fangs…

It has wings…

IT'S A….

Pony Gear

The dragon's snoring is causing the smoke, so the ponies decide to go wake him up. But first, they need to gear up! Use your stickers to match the ponies to the right supplies.

Pony Expedition

Although the ponies are a bit nervous about meeting a dragon, they know they'll be okay if they stick together. Decorate the scene with your stickers.

14 15

16

12

13

A Royal Wedding

Princess Celestia has asked Twilight Sparkle and her friends to help prepare Canterlot for a royal wedding. Use your stickers to see which task each pony has been assigned.

Catering

Music

Wedding Dress

Party

Organizing

Sonic Rainboom

ALL ABOARD!

The ponies are riding the Friendship Express to Canterlot. Who do they see along the way? Take a look at the scene, and then place your stickers in the right spots.

PARTY PLANNING

The ponies are so excited to help Princess Cadance plan her wedding. They all have lots of great ideas to share! Use your stickers to decorate the scene.

A Charming Couple

Rarity has created some lovely designs for the bride and groom. Help Princess Cadance and Shining Armor try on their outfits by placing your stickers below.

DELIGHTFUL DECORATIONS

Decorating the grand hall for a royal wedding is a big job, but somepony's got to do it! Help Pinkie Pie decorate by placing your stickers in the scene.

READING TIME

There sure are lots of amazing books in the Crystal Empire Library! Help Twilight Sparkle and Spike count the colorful books, and then place your stickers in the right spots.

Sparkling Patterns

The ponies are having so much fun exploring the Crystal Empire! Use your stickers to complete the patterns in each row.

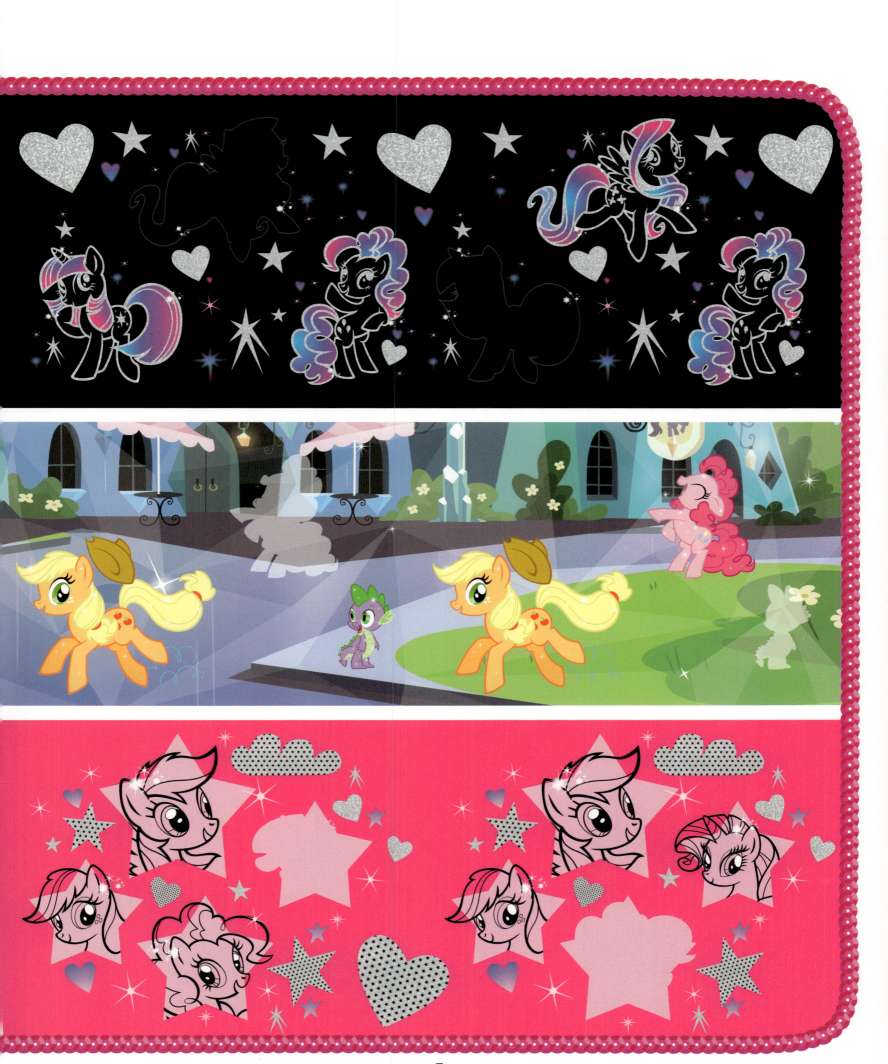

CRYSTAL CASTLE

The pony pals are impressed with everything in the Crystal Empire—especially the magnificent castle! Use your stickers to decorate the scene.

PONY PRIZES

There are lots of prizes to win at the Crystal Faire. Place your stickers in the right spots to see which trophy each of these ponies won.

Hardworking Harvester

Best Fashion Advice

Cheers Up Everypony

Helpful Friend

King Sombra is trying to take over the Crystal Empire! Help the ponies stop the evil king by using your stickers to recreate the top scene in the space below.

AROUND THE EMPIRE

There are lots of things to see around the Crystal Empire! Help Pinkie Pie identify what's what by reading the labels and placing your stickers next to the matching close-up clues.

A Weather Vane

A Statue

The Castle

The Empire's Flag

The Crystal Heart

A History Book

Royal Ponies

How well do you know these royal ponies? Read the labels, and then place your pony and cutie mark stickers over the matching shadows.

Princess Celestia
Co-ruler of Equestria

Princess Luna
Co-ruler of Equestria

Princess Cadance
Defender of the Crystal Empire

King Sombra
Tyrant of the Crystal Empire

FUN AT THE FAIRE

Running the Crystal Faire sure is hard work! Learn what Twilight Sparkle and her friends do to make the day fun by reading the clues below.

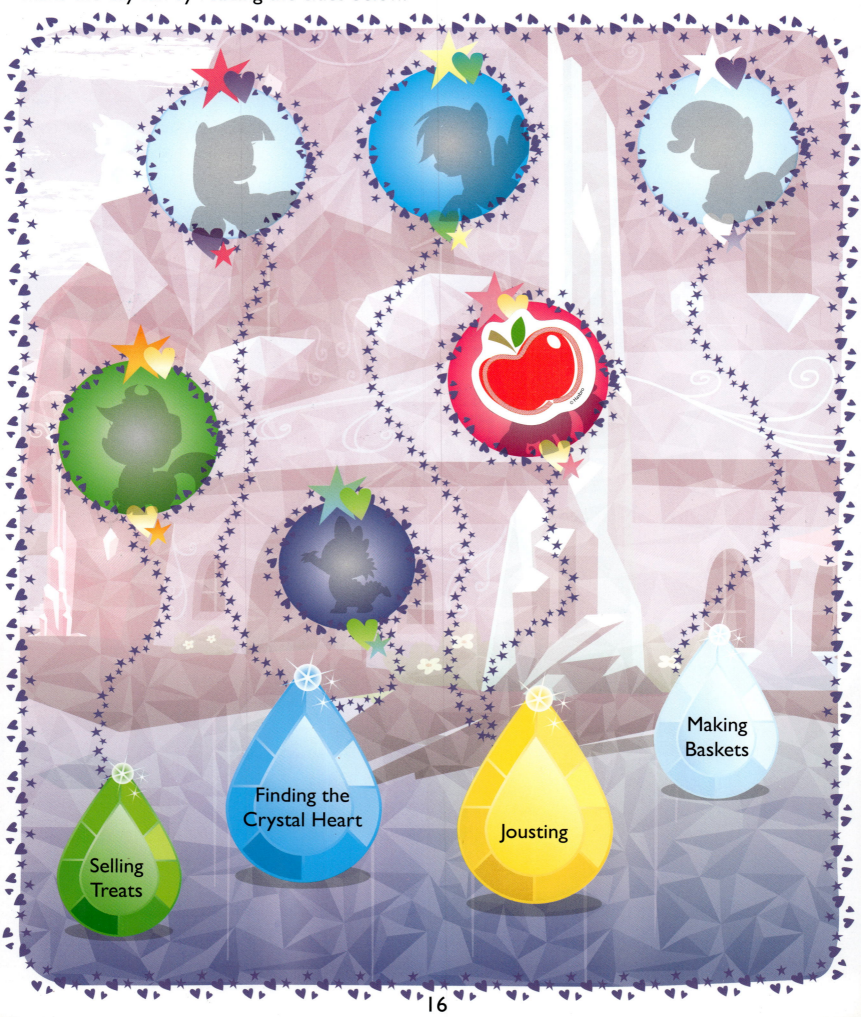